Our
Old Fashioned
Country Diary
— for —
1986

edited by
Linda Campbell Franklin

designed by
Deborah Bracken

design assistants
McKeven Shaunessey and Pattie Silver

Tree Communication, Inc.
New York

Published in the United States of America

Cover illustration by Judith Sutton

ISBN 0-93504-51-2

This book was typeset in Goudy Old Style by
Tree Communications
New York, NY 10001

Dear Friends

If you were with us last year, you'll know that I asked you all to spend part of every day *thinking*. I'm sure that by now you have really thought—and learned—a lot! This year we can relax a bit, and spend part of every day trying to give pleasure where it's needed. And, as it says so well on a button given me by a friend, "Don't postpone joy."

   May your 1986 be a year of love and understanding, joy in small things, admiration of great things, as well as a lot of good fortune, good health and happy memories!

Sincerely,

Linda Campbell Franklin

Our
Portrait Gallery

Jump, grin, smile, pout;
Still, spin, inside, out;
Serious, happy, sad, silly;
Year's start, year's end, willy-nilly.

Looking Forward
in 1986

Tho' some things are planned, do not be surprised,
If nineteen-eighty-six isn't comprised
Of some of the following deeds and events...
Even if now they don't make sense!

Not fishing nor baiting:
Just wishing and waiting.

The New Year

Tuesday & Wednesday, December 31 & January 1

Weather that ushered in the New Year:

*Hopes &
Resolutions*

*The New Year's Eve
Celebration*

A Good Way to Spend New Year's Day

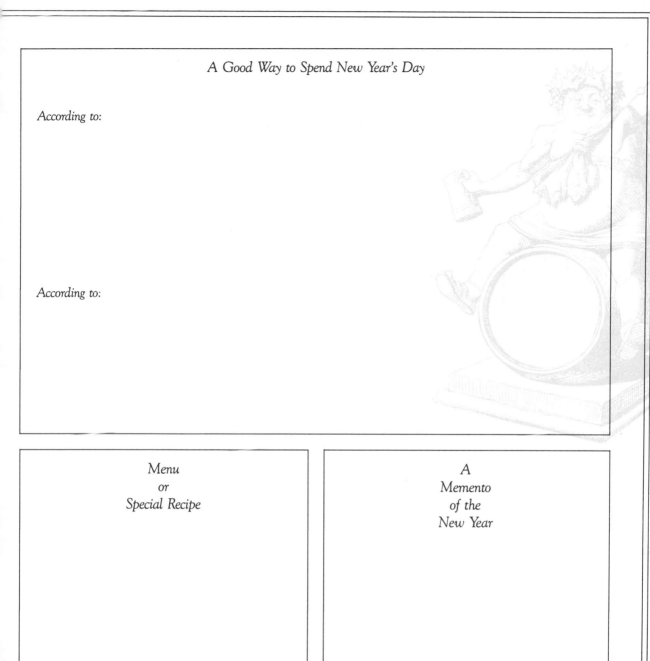

According to:

According to:

Menu
or
Special Recipe

A
Memento
of the
New Year

January

Sun Mon Tue Wed Thur Fri Sat
1 2 3 4
5 6 7 8 9 10 11
12 13 14 15 16 17 18
19 20 21 22 23 24 25
26 27 28 29 30 31

Appointments
30 Monday *Novelist Rudyard Kipling born, 1865* *Philanthropist Simon Guggenheim born, 1867*
31 Tuesday *New Year's Eve. Happy 1986!* *Hogmanay, a Scottish holiday. Sing "Auld Lang Syne"!*
1 Wednesday *New Year's Day* *Football Day: Hike, one, two, three!* *Flag-sewer Betsy Ross born, 1752*
2 Thursday *Patriot Nathaniel Bacon born, 1647*
3 Friday *Women's rights leader, Lucretia Coffin Mott, born, 1793* *Author of* The Hobbit, *J.R.R. Tolkien, born, 1892*
4 Saturday *Fairy tale writer Jacob Grimm born, 1785* *Touch-reading-system inventor Louis Braille born, 1809*
5 Sunday *Twelfth Night*

"It was but natural for the ancient prophets and augurs to consult the heavens when seeking inspiration to guide their steps; much could they find there to help them; they made capital from fortunate eclipses and conjunctions. The wise farmer and sailor still get their warnings from the sky today."

Stephen F. Hamblin, Man's Spiritual Contact with the Landscape, *1923*

All thought, all desires,
   That are under the sun,
Are one with their fires,
   As we also are one:
All matter, all spirit,
   All fashion, all frame,
Receive and inherit
   Their strength from the same.

* * *

From "An Astrologer's Song," by Rudyard Kipling

December January

Diary

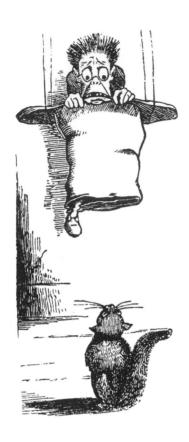

January

Sun Mon Tue Wed Thur Fri Sat
              1 2 3 4
 5 6 7 8 9 10 11
12 13 14 15 16 17 18
19 20 21 22 23 24 25
26 27 28 29 30 31

Appointments
6 Monday *Twelfth Day—The Feast of the Epiphany* *Sherlock Holmes' Birthday*
7 Tuesday *Spooky cartoonist Charles Addams born, 1912* *Jackie Gleason's "Cavalcade of Stars" show first aired, 1950*
8 Wednesday *Crooner Elvis Presley born, 1935*
9 Thursday *League of Women Voters' founder Carrie Catt born, 1859* *Chief Golden Gate Bridge builder Joseph Baermann Strauss born, 1870*
10 Friday *Revolutionary hero Ethan Allen—"Green Mountain Boys"—born, 1737/8* *League of Nations founded, 1920*
11 Saturday *Statesman Alexander Hamilton born in West Indies, 1757* *Philosopher & religious psychologist William James born, 1842*
12 Sunday *Massachusetts Bay Colony Puritan governor John Winthrop, born, 1588* *Call of the Wild author Jack London born, 1876*

"Fear rises out of all darkness, fear for us who are diurnal, not nocturnal animals. But I do not experience this sensation out of doors, as many people do. Night terrors are bred in closets, beds, cellars, attics, and all those traps and pits and sinks in which civilized man houses himself, blunts his senses and breeds his own ills. Out in the open night it may be cold, or windy, or rainy, but it is never anything in which a bogy could endure.

"Indeed, if you think of night in the true, philosophical proportion, you must realize that it is the prevailing, the absolute thing. Light, day, burning suns and stars—all are the exception. They are but gleaming jewels spattered on the black cloth of darkness. Throughout the universe and eternity it is night that prevails. It is the mother of cosmos, capacious womb of light."

Donald Culross Peattie, An Almanac for Moderns, *1935*

January

Diary

January

Sun	Mon	Tue	Wed	Thur	Fri	Sat
				1	2	3 4
5	6	7	8	9	10	11
12	13	14	15	16	17	18
19	20	21	22	23	24	25
26	27	28	29	30	31	

"Write it on your heart that every day is the best day in the year. No man has earned anything rightly until he knows that every day is doomsday. Today is a king in disguise. Today always looks mean to the thoughtless, in the face of a uniform experience that all good and great and happy actions are made up precisely of these blank todays. Let us not be deceived, let us unmask the king as he passes."

Ralph Waldo Emerson

"Both man and womankind belie their nature when they are not kind."

Philip James Bailey

Appointments
13 Monday
Stephen Foster Memorial Day (first celebrated 1952) *Author Horatio Alger born, 1834*
14 Tuesday
Physician & missionary surgeon Albert Schweitzer born, 1875 *Henry Ford's first assembly line began operations, 1914*
15 Wednesday
French dramatist Molière baptized, 1622 *Leader & visionary Martin Luther King, Jr., born, 1929*
16 Thursday
Singer Ethel Merman born, 1909 *Baseball's Dizzy Dean born, 1911*
17 Friday
St. Anthony's Day—Bless the Animals *Inventor, printer, statesman Benjamin Franklin born, 1706*
18 Saturday
Lexicographer Peter Mark Roget, famed for Thesaurus, born, 1779 *American statesman & orator Daniel Webster born, 1782*
19 Sunday
Scottish inventor of steam power, James Watt, born, 1736 *America's 1st mystery writer, Edgar Allan Poe, born, 1809*

January

January

Sun	Mon	Tue	Wed	Thur	Fri	Sat
				1	2	3	4
5	6	7	8	9	10	11
12	13	14	15	16	17	18
19	20	21	22	23	24	25
26	27	28	29	30	31	

"A great man quotes bravely, and will not draw on his invention when his memory serves him with a word as good."

Ralph Waldo Emerson, from Letters and Social Aims

Growing one's own choice words and fancies
In orange tubs, and beds of pansies;
One's sighs and passionate declarations,
In odorous rhetoric of carnations.

Leigh Hunt, from "Love-Letters Made of Flowers"

Appointments

20 Monday

Martin Luther King Day
Hostages released by Iranians, 1981

21 Tuesday

John Fitch, inventor of 1st working steamboat, born, 1743
Count Basie recorded "One O'Clock Jump," 1942

22 Wednesday

English essayist Francis Bacon born, 1561
Violinist Yehudi Menuhin born, 1916

23 Thursday

Handwriting Day
French impressionist painter, Édouard Manet, born, 1832

24 Friday

Gold discovered at Sutter's Mill, CA, 1848
First Boy Scout troop organized, in England, 1908

25 Saturday

"Auld Lang Syne" poet Robert Burns born in Scotland, 1759
Transcontinental telephone line opened, 1915

26 Sunday

Children's author Mary Mapes Dodge born, 1831
Naturalist Roy Chapman Andrews born, 1884

January

Diary

January

Sun Mon Tue Wed Thur Fri Sat
          1 2 3 4
 5 6 7 8 9 10 11
12 13 14 15 16 17 18
19 20 21 22 23 24 25
26 27 28 29 30 31

See yonder little cloud, / That, borne aloft so tenderly by the wind, / Floats fast away over the snowy peaks!

Henry Wadsworth Longfellow, "Michael Angelo"

"We can watch cloud forms rise and disappear without knowing a bit of meteorology. The most famed of cloud paintings were laid on by the artists' brush when the relation of moisture, temperature and dust in the air were unthought of....I can make the same effect...by stirring up the dust in my room while the sun shines through a hole in the drawn curtain. To know that the sun is merely shining on dust in the air does not help me feel the beauty of the sight, and does rob it of some of its poetry."

Stephen F. Hamblin, Man's Spiritual Contact with the Landscape, 1923

Appointments
27 Monday
Lewis Carroll, creator of Alice in Wonderland, *born, 1832*
Labor leader Samuel Gompers born, 1850
28 Tuesday
English Admiral Sir Francis Drake died, 1596
Pianist Arthur Rubinstein born, 1889
29 Wednesday
Swedish philosopher Emanuel Swedenborg born, 1688
American Revolution leader Thomas Paine born, 1737
30 Thursday
Radio musician/director Walter Damrosch born, 1862
Solidarity Day proclaimed, 1982
31 Friday
Composer Franz Schubert born, 1797
Name day of Russian ballerina Anna Pavlova, born 1885
1 Saturday
Black History Month & American Heart Month begin
National Freedom Day: Lincoln approved 13th Amendment, 1865
2 Sunday
Candlemas Day & Groundhog Day
Violinist Jascha Heifetz born, 1901

January  February

There is a pleasure in the pathless woods
  There is a rapture on the lonely shore,
There is society where none intrudes
  By the deep Sea, and music in its roar.

Lord Byron

Leve fit quod bene fertur onus.
(That load becomes light
which is cheerfully borne.)

Ovid

"Baseball is American in its origin, development and area. It is also American in its dynamic qualities of speed and force, and in the shortness of time required to play a full game and reach a decision. Americans do not love serial games like cricket; in literature they are better at writing short stories than at novels, and they enjoy games where a verdict is soon reached."

William Lyon Phelps, Essays on Things, 1931

February
Sun Mon Tue Wed Thur Fri Sat
1
2 3 4 5 6 7 8
9 10 11 12 13 14 15
16 17 18 19 20 21 22
23 24 25 26 27 28

Appointments
3 Monday Composer Felix Mendelssohn born, 1809 Illustrator Norman Rockwell born, 1894
4 Tuesday Chicago's Van Buren Street Bridge, 1st rolling lift type, opened, 1895 Poet Grace McFarland born, 1941
5 Wednesday Statesman Adlai E. Stevenson born, 1900 Baseball great Hank Aaron born, 1934
6 Thursday Baseball legend Babe Ruth born, 1895
7 Friday Novelist & social critic Charles Dickens born, 1812 American naturalist & painter Louis Agassiz Fuertes born, 1874
8 Saturday Boy Scout Week begins. Boy Scouts founded in America, 1910 Actor Jack Lemmon born, 1925
9 Sunday Chinese New Year, Year of the Tiger, 4684 US Weather Bureau established, 1870

February

Diary

Valentine's Day

Friday, February 14, 1986

Love Begins With

Some Love Songs

e Lovely Weather Today:

A
Memento
of the Day

We, the undersigned, resolve to say
"I love you," each and every day:

February

Sun	Mon	Tue	Wed	Thur	Fri	Sat
						1
2	3	4	5	6	7	8
9	10	11	12	13	14	15
16	17	18	19	20	21	22
23	24	25	26	27	28	

"Nothing can quiet the great voice of the city. All day and all night it sounds on. It is the cry of grief, the hearty shout of labor, laughter, rage and yells, sighs and whisperings, the tramp of feet, the clang of bells, the roar of wheels, all mingled into one deep vast sound, in which single sounds are lost, like so many drops in the ocean."

Henry Ward Beecher, Star Papers, 1855

"Love begins with love."

Jean de la Bruyère

Appointments

10 Monday

Fire extinguisher 1st patented, by Alanson Crane, 1863
Tennis great Bill Tilden born, 1893

11 Tuesday

Shrove Tuesday
Inventor Thomas Alva Edison born, 1847

12 Wednesday

Ash Wednesday
Abraham Lincoln born, 1809. NAACP founded, 1909

13 Thursday

Painter Grant Wood born, 1892
First American magazine, "American Magazine," published, 1741

14 Friday

St. Valentine's Day
English economist Thomas Malthus, Essay on Population, born, 1766

15 Saturday

Astronomer Galileo Galilei born, 1564
Inventor Cyrus Hall McCormick born, 1809

16 Sunday

Dutch botanist Hugo De Vries born, 1848
American critic Van Wyck Brooks born, 1886

February

Diary

Curious Specks on The Snow

"Winter weeds and their wind-blown grist for the hungry birds are responsible for many curious specks on the snow,...but there are two forms of peppered snow which the winter walker occasionally meets with, and which have plainly no connection with weed or copse....It must be confessed that when we find the snow literally peppered with these specks, we may know that there is a birch-tree close by, for the birches are responsible for this winged brood...The white-birch-trees during the winter season are seen to be hanging full of catkins...winter parcels done up ready for the coming spring."

William Hamilton Gibson, Sharp Eyes, A Rambler's Calendar, *1893*

February

Sun	Mon	Tue	Wed	Thur	Fri	Sat
						1
2	3	4	5	6	7	8
9	10	11	12	13	14	15
16	17	18	19	20	21	22
23	24	25	26	27	28	

Appointments

17 Monday

Presidents Day

18 Tuesday

Italian battery inventor, Count Alessandro Volta, born, 1745
Art Nouveau artist Louis Comfort Tiffany born, 1848

19 Wednesday

Polish astronomer Nicolaus Copernicus born, 1473

20 Thursday

Social caricaturist Honoré Daumier born, 1808

21 Friday

Poet W.H. Auden born, 1907
English prelate Cardinal Newman born, 1801

22 Saturday

President George Washington born, 1732
Senator Edward Kennedy born, 1932

23 Sunday

Brotherhood Day
German printer Johannes Gutenberg died, 1468

February

Diary

February

Sun Mon Tue Wed Thur Fri Sat
1
2 3 4 5 6 7 8
9 10 11 12 13 14 15
16 17 18 19 20 21 22
23 24 25 26 27 28

"I do and I must reverence human nature. I bless it for its kind affections. I honor it for its achievements in science and art, and still more for its examples of heroic and saintly virtue. These are marks of a divine origin and the pledges of a celestial inheritance; and I thank God that my own lot is bound up with that of the human race."

William Ellery Channing

"It is a great error, in my opinion, to believe that a government is more firm or assured when it is supported by force, than when founded on affection."

Terence, 185–159 B.C.

Appointments

24 Monday

Fairy tale writer Wilhelm Grimm born, 1786

25 Tuesday

Explorer Francisco de Coronado set off for 7 Cities of Cibola, 1540
Italian tenor Enrico Caruso born, 1873

26 Wednesday

Buffalo Bill & Blueberry Hill Day
William F. Cody born, 1846; Fats Domino born, 1928

27 Thursday

Poet Henry Wadsworth Longfellow born, 1807

28 Friday

Illustrator "Punch", Alice in Wonderland Sir John Tenniel born, 1820
Yellowstone National Park established, 1871

1 Saturday

Red Cross Month & Save Your Vision Week begin
Journalist William Dean Howells born, 1837

2 Sunday

Founder of Bodleian Library, Oxford University,
Sir Thomas Bodley, born, 1545

February March

Diary

"Justice discards party, friendship, kindred, and is therefore always represented as blind.

Joseph Addison

			March			
Sun	Mon	Tue	Wed	Thur	Fri	Sat
						1
2	3	4	5	6	7	8
9	10	11	12	13	14	15
16	17	18	19	20	21	22
23	24	25	26	27	28	29
30	31					

Welcome, wild harbinger of spring!
  To this small nook of earth;
Feeling and fancy fondly cling
  Round thoughts which owe their birth
To thee, and to the humble spot
Where chance has fixed thy lowly lot.

Bernard Barton, "To a Crocus"

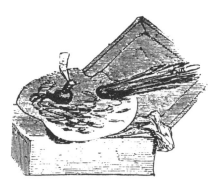

Appointments

3 Monday

Inventor Alexander Graham Bell born, 1847
Painter Vincent van Gogh born, 1853

4 Tuesday

US Constitution declared in effect, 1789
Serfdom abolished in Russia, 1861

5 Wednesday

Crispus Attucks, Black Revolutionary War hero,
killed in Boston Massacre, 1770
Painter & author Howard Pyle born, 1853

6 Thursday

Author & humorist Ring Lardner born, 1885

7 Friday

Animal portraitist Sir Edwin Landseer born, 1802
Botanist Luther Burbank born, 1849

8 Saturday

American jurist Oliver Wendell Holmes, Jr., born, 1841
Famed American typographer & designer, Frederic Goudy, born, 1865

9 Sunday

Hooked Rug Day
Explorer & navigator Amerigo Vespucci born, 1451

March

Diary

March

Sun	Mon	Tue	Wed	Thur	Fri	Sat
						1
2	3	4	5	6	7	8
9	10	11	12	13	14	15
16	17	18	19	20	21	22
23	24	25	26	27	28	29
30	31					

"…When I bear in mind how elegantly we eat our victuals, and remember all the ablutions and preparations and salutations and exclamations and manipulations I performed when I dined out last evening, I reflect what creatures we are of ceremony; how elaborately polite a simian Species."

Logan Pearsall Smith, All Trivia, *1917*

"Why do we take conclusions into our heads for which we have no warrant, and bolt with them like mad horses, until we are brought up by stone walls?"

Charles Dickens, 1856

Appointments

10 Monday

Abolitionist leader Harriet Tubman born, c. 1820
Public health nursing pioneer Lillian Wald born, 1867

11 Tuesday

Johnny Appleseed Day (he died, 1845)
Lawrence "Wunnerful wunnerful" Welk born, 1903

12 Wednesday

New York Times *publisher Adolph S. Ochs born, 1858*
Girl Scouts of America founded, 1912

13 Thursday

Discoverer of oxygen Joseph Priestley born, 1733
Restauranteur Lorenzo Delmonico born, 1813

14 Friday

Railroad engineer Casey Jones born, 1864
Russian novelist Maxim Gorky born, 1868

15 Saturday

Ides of March
The American Legion founded, 1919

16 Sunday

National Wildlife Week begins
First National Library Week opened, 1958

March

Diary

St. Patrick's Day

Monday, March 17, 1986

Today's Weather

Memories That Were Made Today

*'All that glisters,' all that shines out
with hope and cheer, even with a golden glow,
is yet not gold. Rather, our pot o' gold
at the end of the rainbow is filled with:*

Menu or Special Recipe

A Memento of the Day

March

Sun Mon Tue Wed Thur Fri Sat
                        1
2 3 4 5 6 7 8
9 10 11 12 13 14 15
16 17 18 19 20 21 22
23 24 25 26 27 28 29
30 31

O, saw ye the lass wi' the bonnie blue een?
Her smile is the sweetest that ever was seen,
Her cheek like the rose is,
    but fresher, I ween,
She's the loveliest lassie
    that trips on the green.

Richard Ryan

In such green palaces the first kings reign'd.
Slept in their shades, and angels entertain'd;
With such old counsellors they did advise,
And by frequenting sacred groves grew wise.

Edmund Waller, "On St. James' Park"

Appointments

17 Monday

St. Patrick's Day
Camp Fire Girls opened to public membership, 1912

18 Tuesday

Russian composer Nikolai Rimsky-Korsakov born, 1844
German engineer Rudolph Diesel (invented diesel engine) born, 1858

19 Wednesday

Missionary explorer David Livingston born, 1813.
We don't presume it, we know!

20 Thursday

Earth Day. Vernal Equinox. Spring begins 5:03 p.m. EST
Painter Albert Pinkham Ryder born, 1847

21 Friday

Composer Johann Sebastian Bach born, 1685
Composer Modest Mussorgsky born, 1839

22 Saturday

Painter Rosa Bonheur born, 1822
Entrepeneur Florenz Ziegfield born, 1869

23 Sunday

Palm Sunday
First American botanist, John Bartram, born, 1699

March

Diary

Easter

Today's Weather:

Time of Sunrise:

Sunday March 30, 1986

An Easter Celebration

A
*Memento
of the Day*

*Signs
of
Hope*

March

Sun	Mon	Tue	Wed	Thur	Fri	Sat
						1
2	3	4	5	6	7	8
9	10	11	12	13	14	15
16	17	18	19	20	21	22
23	24	25	26	27	28	29
30	31					

Nature
A Minister of Happiness

"It was not meant that the enjoyments of life should be few and intense, but many and gentle; and great happiness is the sum of a multitude of drops. Those days which are the channels of mighty joys are, perhaps, the most memorable. But they exhaust. They unfit us for common duties. We regard them as we do mountain-tops. We go up occasionally, not to dwell there, but to see at a glance the whole of that which, upon the plains, we see only in succession and in detail. But the staple of pleasure must be found in small measures, and in common things."

Henry Ward Beecher, Star Papers, *1855*

Appointments

24 Monday

Craftsman & artist William Morris born, 1834
Geologist & ethnologist John Wesley Powell born, 1834

25 Tuesday

Purim
Conductor Arturo Toscanini born, 1867

26 Wednesday

Poet Alfred Housman born, 1859
Poet Robert Frost born, 1874

27 Thursday

X-Ray discoverer Wilhelm Konrad Roentgen born, 1845
Actress Gloria Swanson born, 1899

28 Friday

Good Friday
Accident at Three Mile Island nuclear plant led to shut-down, 1979

29 Saturday

Holy Saturday
Electric welding inventor Elihu Thomson born, 1853

30 Sunday

Easter
American philosopher John Fiske born, 1842

March

March

Sun	Mon	Tue	Wed	Thur	Fri	Sat
						1
2	3	4	5	6	7	8
9	10	11	12	13	14	15
16	17	18	19	20	21	22
23	24	25	26	27	28	29
30	31					

Appointments

31 Monday

Bunsen burner inventor Robert W. E. Bunsen born, 1811
First US-Japan treaty signed, 1854

1 Tuesday

The rest of the Diary is blank. Ha! Ha! Fooled you!
Blood circulation discoverer William Harvey born, 1578

2 Wednesday

Hans Christian Andersen, fairy tale writer, born, 1805
Russian pianist / composer Sergei Rachmaninoff born, 1873

3 Thursday

Humanitarian Edward Everett Hale born, 1822
Naturalist John Burroughs born, 1837

4 Friday

Photographer of the great Western landmarks,
William Henry Jackson born, 1843

5 Saturday

Black leader Booker T. Washington born, 1856

6 Sunday

Journalist & reformer Lincoln Steffens born, 1866

"Nothing is more exciting in early April than the sound of running water in a brook, no matter how small it is. Something that has been locked has been loosed again, and it behooves each one of us to run and see. The emblem of the returning life activity of spring has come again to us. For many minutes we are content to just look—before any thought comes to us, for we are rapt in a kind of Nature worship that needs no thought expression."

Stephen F. Hamblin, Man's Spiritual Contact with the Landscape, *1923*

"Love is a lock that linketh noble minds, faith is the key that shuts the spring of love."

Robert Greene

March April

Diary

Music is in all growing things;
And underneath the silky wings
  Of smallest insects there is stirred
  A pulse of air that must be heard;
Earth's silence lives, and throbs, and sings.

George Parsons Lathrop

So, if unprejudiced you scan
The goings of this clock-work, man,
You find a hundred movements made
By fine devices in his head;
But 'tis the stomach's solid stroke
That tells his being what's o'clock.

Matthew Prior

April

Sun	Mon	Tue	Wed	Thur	Fri	Sat
		1	2	3	4	5
6	7	8	9	10	11	12
13	14	15	16	17	18	19
20	21	22	23	24	25	26
27	28	29	30			

Appointments

7 Monday

World Health Day
Poet William Wordsworth born, 1770

8 Tuesday

Buddha Day in Hawaii
Explorer Ponce de Leon landed near St. Augustine, FL, 1513

9 Wednesday

Violinist Efrem Zimbalist born, 1889
Singer & actor Paul Robeson born, 1898

10 Thursday

Essayist William Hazlitt born, 1778
Salvation Army founder William Booth born, 1829

11 Friday

Barbershop Quartet Day
Jackie Robinson 1st black to play major leagues—Brooklyn Dodgers, 1947

12 Saturday

Cosmonaut Yuri Gagarin 1st man in space, for 108 minutes, 1961

13 Sunday

Eli Terry, great clockmaker & inventor, born, 1772

April

Diary

April

Sun	Mon	Tue	Wed	Thur	Fri	Sat
		1	2	3	4	5
6	7	8	9	10	11	12
13	14	15	16	17	18	19
20	21	22	23	24	25	26
27	28	29	30			

"…No flower can be so strange, or so new, that a friendliness does not spring up at once between you. You gather them up along your rambles; and sit down to make their acquaintance on some shaded bank with your feet over the brook, where your shoes feed their vanity as in a mirror. You assort them; you questions their graces; you enjoy their odor; you range them on the grass in a row and look from one to another; you gather them up, and study a fit gradation of colors, and search for new specimens to fill the degrees between too violent extremes. All the while, and it is a long while, if the day be gracious and leisure ample, various suggestions and analogies of life are darting in and out of your mind."

Henry Ward Beecher, Star Papers, *1855*

Appointments

14 Monday

Keep on looking for Halley's comet in the morning sky
Noah Webster's Dictionary *published, 1828*

15 Tuesday

(We won't mention taxes)
Painter Thomas Hart Benton born, 1889

16 Wednesday

Arbor Day in many states
Arctic explorer Sir John Franklin born, 1786

17 Thursday

Philanthropist & book collector John Pierpont Morgan born, 1837
Playwright Thornton Wilder born, 1897

18 Friday

Conductor Leopold Stokowski born, 1882
Anniversary of 1906 San Francisco Earthquake observed at 5:13 a.m.

19 Saturday

Patriots' Day—Revolutionary War began, 1775

20 Sunday

Daniel Chester French, sculptor of Lincoln memorial statue born, 1850

A*pril*

Diary

April

Sun	Mon	Tue	Wed	Thur	Fri	Sat
		1	2	3	4	5
6	7	8	9	10	11	12
13	14	15	16	17	18	19
20	21	22	23	24	25	26
27	28	29	30			

"A man absorbed in the study of grasses tramples down oaks unwittingly in his walks."

Henry David Thoreau

"The only faith that wears well and holds its color in all weathers is that which is woven of conviction and set with the sharp mordant of experience."

James Russell Lowell

"There is no bird sound like it, this soft, murmurous tattoo of the grouse in the bare, freshening woods. It is in harmony with the first heart-throbs and accelerating life of exuberant awakening nature—the quickening seeds, the flowing sap, the swelling buds."

William Hamilton Gibson

Appointments
21 Monday
Humorist Josh Billings born, 1818
Naturalist & conservationist John Muir born, 1838
22 Tuesday
Metaphysician Immanuel Kant born, 1724
Novelist Ellen Glasgow born, 1874
23 Wednesday
Poet dramatist William Shakespeare born, 1564
1st motion picture shown, Koster & Beal Music Hall, NYC, 1896
24 Thursday
Passover
Novelist Anthony Trollope born, 1815
25 Friday
Wireless telegraphy inventor Guglielmo Marconi born, 1874
26 Saturday
Naturalist painter (who killed birds to paint them, alas), John James Audubon, born, 1785
Landscape architect Frederick Law Olmsted born, 1822
27 Sunday
Daylight Savings begins. "Spring ahead," at 2 a.m.
Telegraph inventor & artist Samuel Finley Breese Morse born, 1791

April

Diary

"Mother"—a word that holds the tender spell
Of all the dear essential things of earth;
A home, clean sunlit rooms, and the good smell
Of bread; a table spread; a glowing hearth.
And love beyond the dream of anyone....
I search for words for her...and there
are none.

Grace Noll Crowell

April

Sun	Mon	Tue	Wed	Thur	Fri	Sat
		1	2	3	4	5
6	7	8	9	10	11	12
13	14	15	16	17	18	19
20	21	22	23	24	25	26
27	28	29	30			

Appointments

28 Monday

Actor Lionel Barrymore born, 1878

29 Tuesday

Sculptor Lorado Taft born, 1860
London Philharmonic founder Sir Thomas Beecham born, 1879

30 Wednesday

Radio's "Queen for a Day" first aired, 1945

1 Thursday

May Day, Law Day, Lei Day
Landscape painter George Inness born, 1825

2 Friday

Hudson's Bay Company chartered, 1670
Great friend & doctor of children Benjamin Spock born, 1903

3 Saturday

Kentucky Derby
Photographer & reformer Jacob August Riis born, 1849
Friends of Animals founded, 1957

4 Sunday

Be Kind to Animals Week begins
Educator Horace Mann born, 1796

April May

Diary

Mother's Day

Sunday May 11, 1986

Today's weather:

*A
Memento
of the Day*

*Menu
or Special Recipe*

Special Memories
of
Mothers

Promises to Keep

			May			
Sun	Mon	Tue	Wed	Thur	Fri	Sat
					1	2 3
4	5	6	7	8	9	10
11	12	13	14	15	16	17
18	19	20	21	22	23	24
25	26	27	28	29	30	31

She answered by return of post
The invitation of her host.
She caught the train she said she would,
And changed at junctions as she should.
She brought a light and smallish box
and keys belonging to the locks.

* * *

She left no little things behind
Excepting loving thoughts and kind.

Rose Henniker Heaton, "The Perfect Guest"

Appointments

5 Monday

German social philosopher Karl Marx born, 1818
Author Christopher Morley born, 1890

6 Tuesday

Explorer and aviator over North Pole, Richard E. Byrd, born, 1888
Sigmund ·Freud born, 1856

7 Wednesday

Poet Robert Browning born, 1812
Russian composer Peter Ilyitch Tchaikovsky born, 1840

8 Thursday

Ascension Day
Explorer De Soto discovered Old Man River—The Mississippi—1541

9 Friday

Mother's Day 1st proclaimed, by President Wilson, 1914
Abolitionist John Brown born, 1800

10 Saturday

Save American Trains Day
Union Pacific & Central Pacific railroads joined in Utah, 1869

11 Sunday

Mother's Day
Rogation Sunday

May

Diary

May

Sun	Mon	Tue	Wed	Thur	Fri	Sat
					1	2 3
4	5	6	7	8	9	10
11	12	13	14	15	16	17
18	19	20	21	22	23	24
25	26	27	28	29	30	31

Entertaining Posterity

"Good heaven, to think of the amount of work [Posterity] will have to get through! Only to read all those books, to contemplate all those pictures and statues, and to listen to all that music, so generously bequeathed to him by crowds of admiring legatees through many generations, will be no slight labour...Then the numbers of ingenious inventions he will have to test, prove, and adopt, from the perpetual motion to the long range, will necessarily consume some of the best years of his life...Hence...if he *must* be so overworked, let us at least so something to entertain him....I am sorry to say that I don't think we do enough to make him smile. It appears to me that we might tickle him a little more."

Charles Dickens

Appointments
12 Monday
Humorist, limerist & artist Edward Lear born, 1812
Nurse Florence Nightgale born, 1820
13 Tuesday
Glassmaker Henry William Stiegel born, 1729
Boxer Joe Louis born, 1914
14 Wednesday
Mercury thermometer physicist Gabriel Daniel Fahrenheit born, 1686
Founder of New Harmony, IN community, Robert Owen, born, 1771
15 Thursday
L. Frank Baum, author of Wizard of Oz, born, 1856
780,000 pairs of nylon stockings sold 1st day on sale, 1940
16 Friday
French novelist Honoré de Balzac born, 1799
Actor Henry Fonda born, 1905
17 Saturday
Preakness Stakes
Vaccination discoverer Dr. Edward Jenner born, 1749
18 Sunday
Pentecost
World Good-Will Day. Hague Peace Conference 1st opened, 1899

May

Diary

May
Sun Mon Tue Wed Thur Fri Sat
1 2 3
4 5 6 7 8 9 10
11 12 13 14 15 16 17
18 19 20 21 22 23 24
25 26 27 28 29 30 31

"The example of the bird does not prove that man can fly....Imagine the proud possessor of the aeroplane darting through the air at a speed of several hundred feet per second! It is the speed alone that sustains him. How is he ever going to stop?"

Simon Newcomb, 1901

"There is no beautifier of complexion, or form, or behavior, like the wish to scatter joy and not pain around us."

Ralph Waldo Emerson

Appointments

19 Monday

Victoria Day
Naturalist & animal sculptor Carl Akeley born, 1864

20 Tuesday

International Bureau of Weights & Measures formed, 1875
Microphone & phonograph record inventor Emile Berliner born, 1851

21 Wednesday

American Red Cross organized, Clara Barton president, 1881
Jazz pianist & composer Fats Waller born, 1904

22 Thursday

National Maritime Day
Composer Richard Wagner born, 1813

23 Friday

Botanist Carl von Linné—Linnaeus—born, 1707

24 Saturday

Queen Victoria of England born, 1819
Engineer John Augustus Roebling's Brooklyn Bridge opened, 1883

25 Sunday

Poetry Week
Essayist, poet & philosopher Ralph Waldo Emerson born, 1803

M*ay*

Diary

Memorial Day

We observed the day on May   , 1986

Today's weather:

Special Things to Remember

A Memento of the Day

Some Favorite Quotations for the Day

May

Sun	Mon	Tue	Wed	Thur	Fri	Sat
					1	2 3
4	5	6	7	8	9	10
11	12	13	14	15	16	17
18	19	20	21	22	23	24
25	26	27	28	29	30	31

"Like meadow flowers planted by the wind, a year or more before, bright, wispy, odd and wild memories will suddenly appear—surrounded by the more cultivated sorts of plain green grass and manicured lawns, and neat herbaceous rows.

Grace McFarland

"It [grass] is the handkerchief of the Lord."

Walt Whitman

Appointments
26 Monday
Memorial Day, in all but 8 states *Author Alexander Pushkin born, 1799*
27 Tuesday
Dancer Isadora Duncan born, 1878 *Engineer Joseph B. Strauss's Golden Gate Bridge opened, 1937*
28 Wednesday
Dionne Quintuplets born in Quebec, 1934
29 Thursday
Author G.K. Chesterton born, 1874
30 Friday
Memorial Day, traditional observance since 1868 *"Pennsylvania Evening Post," 1st US daily paper, published, 1783*
31 Saturday
Walt Whitman, poet of Leaves of Grass, born, 1819 *The Johnstown Flood, 1889*
1 Sunday
Pat-a-Cat Day *America's 1st book fair held in NYC, 1801*

May June

Diary

June						
Sun	Mon	Tue	Wed	Thur	Fri	Sat
	1	2	3	4	5	6	7
8	9	10	11	12	13	14
15	16	17	18	19	20	21
22	23	24	25	26	27	28
29	30					

"Whatever philosophy may determine of material nature, it is certainly true of intellectual nature, that it abhors a vacuum."

Samuel Johnson

"Public parks...fall in the same category with the lawn; they too, at their best, are imitations of the pasture. Such a park is of course best kept by grazing, and the cattle on the grass are themselves no mean addition to the beauty of the thing....[It is] an expression of the pecuniary element in popular taste, that such a method of keeping public grounds is seldom resorted to....To the average popular apprehension a herd of cattle so pointedly suggests thrift and usefulness that their presence in the public pleasure ground would be intolerably cheap."

Thorstein Veblen, The Theory of the Leisure Class, *1899*

Appointments
2 Monday
Novelist Thomas Hardy born, 1840
Composer Sir Edward Elgar born, 1857
3 Tuesday
Great tenor Roland Hayes born, 1887
Gemini 4 astronaut Ed White "walked" in space, 1965
4 Wednesday
King George III born, 1738. Where'd we be without him?
83 hours & 34 minutes for 1st through train, NYC to SF, 1876
5 Thursday
Slavery-shaking 1st chapter of Uncle Tom's Cabin,
by Harriet Beecher Stowe, appeared in magazine, 1851
6 Friday
Patriot Nathan Hale born, 1755
Novelist Thomas Mann born, 1875
7 Saturday
Belmont Stakes
Mohammed, Prophet of Islam, died, 632 A.D.
8 Sunday
Architect Frank Lloyd Wright born, 1867

June

Diary

Special Memories
of Fathers

A Memento of the Day

Father's Day

June 15, 1986

Today's Weather:

Promises to Keep

Menu
or
Special Recipe

June						
Sun	Mon	Tue	Wed	Thur	Fri	Sat
1	2	3	4	5	6	7
8	9	10	11	12	13	14
15	16	17	18	19	20	21
22	23	24	25	26	27	28
29	30					

A day for toil, an hour for sport,
But for a friend is life too short.

Ralph Waldo Emerson

Though I am old with wandering / Through
hollow lands and hilly lands, / I will find out
where she has gone, / And kiss her lips and
take her hands; / And walk among long dap-
pled grass, / And pluck till time and times
are done / The silver apples of the
moon, /The golden apples of the sun.

William Butler Yeats

Oh my!l feel just as happy
as a big Sun-flower.

Appointments

9 Monday

Song writer Cole Porter born, 1893

10 Tuesday

Preservation Hall—New Orleans jazz spot—opened, 1961

11 Wednesday

Composer Richard Strauss born, 1864

12 Thursday

Suspension bridge engineer John Augustus Roebling born, 1806
Ornithologist Frank Michler Chapman born, 1864

13 Friday

Shavuoth
First Friday the 13th (and last) in 1986

14 Saturday

Reformer & novelist Harriet Beecher Stowe born, 1811
Photographer of smokestacks & industry Margaret Bourke White born, 1906

15 Sunday

Father's Day
King John signed Magna Carta, 1215
Sculptor Malvina Hoffman born, 1887

June

Diary

June

Sun	Mon	Tue	Wed	Thur	Fri	Sat
1	2	3	4	5	6	7
8	9	10	11	12	13	14
15	16	17	18	19	20	21
22	23	24	25	26	27	28
29	30					

"Nothing can bring back the hour of splendour in the grass, of glory in the flower."

William Wordsworth

In lang, lang days o' simmer,
   When the clear and cloudless sky
Refuses ae wee drap o' rain
   To Nature parched and dry,
The genial night, wi' balmy breath
   Gars verdure spring anew,
An' ilka blade o' grass
   Keps its ain drap o' dew.

James Ballantine

Appointments
16 Monday
The World Court organized, 1920
17 Tuesday
Old Man River—the Mississippi—discovered again, by Jolliet & Marquette, 1673
18 Wednesday
Owner of land where gold discovered, John August Sutter, died, 1880   *Battle of Waterloo, 1815*
19 Thursday
NY Yankee Lou Gehrig born, 1903
20 Friday
Great Seal of the US, with eagle, 1st approved, 1782
21 Saturday
Summer Solstice, Summer begins: 12:30 p.m. EDT   *Artist noted for book illustrations, Rockwell Kent, born, 1882*
22 Sunday
Author Anne Morrow Lindbergh born, 1907

June

Diary

June

Sun	Mon	Tue	Wed	Thur	Fri	Sat
1	2	3	4	5	6	7
8	9	10	11	12	13	14
15	16	17	18	19	20	21
22	23	24	25	26	27	28
29	30					

"How could an actual person fit into the covers of a book? The book is not a continent, not a definite geographical measure, it cannot contain so huge a thing as an actual full-size person. Any person has to be scaled by eliminations to fit the book world."

Pearl S. Buck

Children's Play

"They are up and fledged by breakfast, and then they are off in uncircumscribed liberty till dinner....They can build all manner of structures in wet sand, or paddle in the water, and even get their feet wet, their clothes dirty, or their pantaloons torn, without being aught reckoned against them."

Henry Ward Beecher, Star Papers, *1855*

Appointments

23 Monday

William Sholes patented his typewriter, 1868

24 Tuesday

Fête Nationale in Quebec
Preacher & writer Henry Ward Beecher born, 1813

25 Wednesday

George Orwell, author & social satirist, born, 1903
Wages & Hours Act signed, 1938; 44 hours a week at 20¢ an hour!

26 Thursday

UN Charter signed by 50 countries, 1945

27 Friday

Writer (though blind and deaf) Helen Keller born, 1880

28 Saturday

Founder of Methodism, John Wesley, born, 1703
World War I ends with Versailles Treaty, 1919

29 Sunday

Panama Canal engineer George Washington Goethals born, 1858

June

Diary

Independence
Day

Today's glorious weather:

Picnic Menu
or
Spectatcular Recipe

A Memento of the Day

Freedoms, Rights & Duties

July

Sun	Mon	Tue	Wed	Thur	Fri	Sat
		1	2	3	4	5
6	7	8	9	10	11	12
13	14	15	16	17	18	19
20	21	22	23	24	25	26
27	28	29	30	31		

"The body of John Paul Jones, discovered in a built-over Paris cemetery after a six-year search, was convoyed to the United States by a fleet of American warships, and on July 24, 1905 was landed at Annapolis for burial in the grounds of the Naval Academy."

Mark Sullivan, Our Times, 1927

Build me straight, O worthy Master! /Staunch and strong, a goodly vessel / That shall laugh at all disaster, / And with wave and whirlwind wrestle!

Henry Wadsworth Longfellow, "The Building of the Ship"

Appointments

30 Monday

California granted Yosemite Valley as public park, 1864. Became National Park in 1890

1 Tuesday

Canada Day
Lincoln signed bill subsidizing railroad, 1862. Save our trains!

2 Wednesday

Opera composer von Gluck born, 1714

3 Thursday

Beginning of "Dog Days"
Veteran's Administration created, 1930

4 Friday

Independence Day
Novelist Nathaniel Hawthorne born, 1804

5 Saturday

First Navy Admiral, David Farragut, born, 1801
Circus entrepeneur Phineas Taylor Barnum born, 1810

6 Sunday

Revolutionary naval hero John Paul Jones born, 1747

June **July**

Diary

July

Sun Mon Tue Wed Thur Fri Sat
            1 2 3 4 5
 6 7 8 9 10 11 12
13 14 15 16 17 18 19
20 21 22 23 24 25 26
27 28 29 30 31

"Inner harmony is attained only when, by some means, terms are made with the environment. When it occurs on any other than an 'objective' basis, it is illusory—in extreme cases to the point of insanity. Fortunately for variety in experience, terms are made in many ways—ways ultimately decided by selective interest. Pleasures may come about through chance contact and stimulation; such pleasures are not to be despised in a world full of pain. But happiness and delight are a different sort of thing. They come to be through a fulfillment that reaches to the depths of our being—one that is an adjustment of our whole being with the conditions of existence.

John Dewey, Man and Art, *1934*

Appointments

7 Monday

Louis Armstrong recorded "Alexander's Ragtime Band,"
& Count Basie recorded "One O'Clock Jump," 1937

8 Tuesday

French fablist Jean de la Fontaine born, 1621
US issued 1st passport, to Francis Barre, 1796

9 Wednesday

National Fast Day inaugurated, 1832
Electrical inventor Nikola Tesla born, 1856. Did Niagara power station.

10 Thursday

Religious reformer John Calvin born, 1509
Painter James Abbott McNeill Whistler born, 1834

11 Friday

Store-founder par excellence John Wanamaker born, 1838

12 Saturday

Naturalist & diary-keeper Henry David Thoreau born, 1817
Photographic pioneer George Eastman born, 1854

13 Sunday

Sir Kenneth Clark, creator of TV's "Civilization," born, 1903

July

Diary

Fate

Once I planted some potatoes
  In my garden fair and bright;
    Unelated
    Long I waited,
  And no sprout appeared in sight.

But my "peachblows" in the cellar,
  On the cold and grimy flag
    All serenely
    Sprouted greenly
  In an ancient paper bag

R.K. Munkittrick

But, alas! alas! for the women's fate,
Who has from a mob to choose a mate!
'Tis a strange and painful mystery!
But the more the eggs the worse the hatch:
The more the fish, the worse the catch;
The more the sparks the worse the match;
Is a fact in woman's history.

Thomas Hood, "Miss Kilmansegg. Her Courtship"

July

Sun	Mon	Tue	Wed	Thur	Fri	Sat
		1	2	3	4	5
6	7	8	9	10	11	12
13	14	15	16	17	18	19
20	21	22	23	24	25	26
27	28	29	30	31		

Appointments

14 Monday

First Esperanto book published, 1887

15 Tuesday

English architect Inigo Jones born, 1573
Great painting master Rembrandt van Rijn born, 1606

16 Wednesday

South Pole discoverer (1911) Roald Amundsen born, 1872

17 Thursday

Hymn writer Isaac Watts born, 1674
"Punch", oldest humorous periodical, 1st published, in London, 1841

18 Friday

Novelist William Makepeace Thackeray born, 1811
Playwright Clifford Odets born, 1906

19 Saturday

First Woman's Rights Convention in US convened, Seneca Falls, NY, 1848
Radio's "Our Miss Brooks" first aired, 1948

20 Sunday

Mountaineer Sir Edmund Percival Hillary
(1st to conquer Everest) born, 1919

July

Diary

"I like a bit of a mongrel myself, whether it's a man or a dog; they're the best for every day."

George Bernard Shaw

July

Sun	Mon	Tue	Wed	Thur	Fri	Sat
		1	2	3	4	5
6	7	8	9	10	11	12
13	14	15	16	17	18	19
20	21	22	23	24	25	26
27	28	29	30	31		

"Waves upon the beach—they are as nothing to the scientist, yet the fool and the philosopher listen to them daily and read from them more than a moving show of forms and colors. You can explain waves, but you cannot explain the changes in yourself as you sit silent at their feet. They roll in upon me from beyond my ken, and will roll on in their own way when I am long gone beyond them and know them no more; yet something in them has ever been with me, is felt today within me though wind blow high or low, and a kinship with them in me will go forward in my soul forever."

Stephen F. Hamblin, Man's Spiritual Contact with the Landscape, *1923*

Appointments

21 Monday

Adventurer/novelist Ernest Hemingway born, 1899

22 Tuesday

Moses Cleaveland settled on site of Cleveland OH, *1796*
Poet Stephen Vincent Benét born, 1898

23 Wednesday

America's 1st swimming school opened, in Boston, 1828

24 Thursday

Aviatrix Amelia Earhart born, 1898

25 Friday

Constitution Day in Puerto Rico
Theatrical genius David Belasco born, 1853

26 Saturday

The US*'s first postmaster—Benjamin Franklin—appointed, 1775*

27 Sunday

First permanent Atlantic telegraph cable completed, 1866
Korean War ended, 1953

July

Diary

"They were upon their great theme: 'When I get to be a man!' Being human, though boys, they considered their present estate too commonplace to be dwelt upon. So, when the old men gather, they say: 'When I was a boy!' It really is the land of nowadays that we never discover."

Booth Tarkington, Pernod

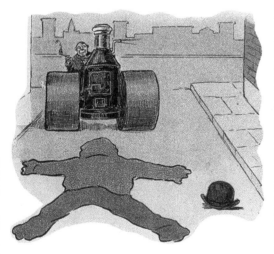

Hope springs eternal in the human breast; Man never *is*, but always *to be* blest.

Alexander Pope, Essay on Man

August

Sun	Mon	Tue	Wed	Thur	Fri	Sat
					1	2
3	4	5	6	7	8	9
10	11	12	13	14	15	16
17	18	19	20	21	22	23
24	25	26	27	28	29	30
31						

Appointments

28 Monday

29 Tuesday

Booth Tarkington born, 1869

30 Wednesday

Henry Ford born, 1863

31 Thursday

1 Friday

Francis Scott Key born, 1779

2 Saturday

3 Sunday

July August

Diary

Neat and Perfect Picnics

"The most important thing about a picnic is water for tea. Usually there is a cottage near the place, where water may be drawn, and possibly where it may be boiled too; otherwise water has to be taken. It is always well to find out beforehand about water. Many a picnic has been spoiled for want of this preparation; people baulked of their tea, or kept waiting for it until over-tired, being poor company. Milk has also be to thought of in advance. Two things which are usually very necessary at a picnic are a corkscrew and a box of what are called flaming vestas—matches that will keep alight in a wind. There cannot be too clear an understanding as to who is to take food, and what kind and amount each is to take. Many squires and landowners have shut their parks to picnic parties because of the hateful mess of paper and bottles which was found after they had left."

E.V. Lucas & Elizabeth Lucas, Three Hundred Games and Pastimes, *1900*

August

Sun	Mon	Tue	Wed	Thur	Fri	Sat
					1	2
3	4	5	6	7	8	9
10	11	12	13	14	15	16
17	18	19	20	21	22	23
24	25	26	27	28	29	30
31						

Appointments

4 Monday

US *Coast Guard Day. Coast Guard founded, 1790*
Chautauqua Literary & Scientific Circle founded, 1874

5 Tuesday

Law creating 1st federal income tax signed, 1861

6 Wednesday

US *Weather Bureau Chief Francis Wilton Reichelderfer born, 1895*

7 Thursday

Peace Bridge opened between US and Canada, 1927

8 Friday

America's 1st professional architect Charles Bulfinch born, 1763
Poet Sara Teasdale born, 1884

9 Saturday

First televised tennis tournament, Eastern Grass Court from Rye, NY, 1939
The Compleat Angler, Izaak Walton, born, 1593

10 Sunday

Smithsonian Institution established, 1846

August

Diary

August

Sun	Mon	Tue	Wed	Thur	Fri	Sat
					1	2
3	4	5	6	7	8	9
10	11	12	13	14	15	16
17	18	19	20	21	22	23
24	25	26	27	28	29	30
31						

To Seal Our Friendship

*May the seal of True
Friendship
Between us be found,
As long as we live,
And the world
goes round.*

"I will readily allow that accident has had much to do with the origin of the arts as with the progress of the sciences. But it has been by scientific processes and experiments that these accidental results have been rendered really applicable to the purposes of common life. Besides, it requires a certain degree of knowledge and scientific combination to understand and seize upon the facts which have originated in accident."

Sir Humphrey Davy, Consolations in Travel, *1830*

"Wherever the institution of private property is found, even in a slightly developed form, the economic process bears the character of a struggle between men for the possession of goods."

Thorstein Veblen, The Theory of the Leisure Class, *1899*

Appointments

11 Monday

Americ's 1st forester/conservationist Gifford Pinchot born, 1865

12 Tuesday

Author Mary Roberts Rinehart born, 1876
Discoverer of animal camouflage Abbott Handerson Thayer, born, 1849

13 Wednesday

First English printer William Caxton born, c. 1422
Antislavery reformer Lucy Stone born, 1818

14 Thursday

President Roosevelt signed law creating Social Security, 1935

15 Friday

Actress Ethel Barrymore born, 1879
Panama Canal officially opened, 1914

16 Saturday

Discovery Day in Yukon Province. Gold discovered there, 1896

17 Sunday

First successful transatlantic balloon flight, 1978

August

Diary

Sweet Sounds

"Another thing that the farmer's wife will very likely let you do is to 'ring' the bees when they swarm. 'Ringing' the bees is beating a tin pot or a shovel with a stick close to the swarm. The sound is supposed, by some country-people, to stupefy or please them, and thus check any desire to fly off; but many beemasters think it useless. Very likely the practice has come down from the old days before sugar was cheap—when every one wanted honey for sweetening purposes and therefore most persons kept bees.... 'Ringing' probably was then meant to announce to the neighbors that your bees were swarming, so that it would be more easy to claim them if they strayed to another's ground."

E.V. Lucas & Elizabeth Lucas, Three Hundred Games and Pastimes, *1900*

August

Sun	Mon	Tue	Wed	Thur	Fri	Sat
					1	2
3	4	5	6	7	8	9
10	11	12	13	14	15	16
17	18	19	20	21	22	23
24	25	26	27	28	29	30
31						

Appointments

18 Monday

Merchant & philanthropist Marshall Field, founder of Chicago's Natural History Museum, born, 1834

19 Tuesday

Clock maker Seth Thomas born, 1785
Patent for condensed milk granted, 1856

20 Wednesday

Newspaperman Edgar A. Guest born, 1881

21 Thursday

Debates between Lincoln & Douglas began, 1858

22 Friday

Composer Claude Debussy born, 1862
Fantasy writer Ray Bradbury born, 1920

23 Saturday

The 6-story Fifth Avenue Hotel, 1st with elevator, opened in NYC, 1859
Dancer Gene Kelly born, 1912

24 Sunday

Architect Charles Follen McKim (J.P. Morgan Library, NYC) born, 1847

August

KARAT & DIAL,
CLOCK AND WATCHMAKERS.

AGENTS FOR

Ladies' Year-Delaying Time-Keepers.

Diary

OUTSTOMACH HOTEL,
B. G. PAUNCH, Proprietor.

GOOD LIVING: SWEET BEDS:
LIBERAL CHARGES.

TURKEYVILLE,
W. T.

"The equal right of all men to the use of land is as clear as their equal right to breathe the air—it is a right proclaimed by the fact of their existence. For we cannot suppose that some men have a right to be in this world, and others no right."

Henry George, Progress and Poverty

"Decide not rashly. The decision made can never be recalled. The gods implore not, plead not, solicit not; they only offer choice and occasion, which once being passed return no more."

Henry Wadsworth Longfellow

August

Sun	Mon	Tue	Wed	Thur	Fri	Sat
					1	2
3	4	5	6	7	8	9
10	11	12	13	14	15	16
17	18	19	20	21	22	23
24	25	26	27	28	29	30
31						

Appointments

25 Monday

Detective Allan Pinkerton born, 1819
Author & poet Bret Harte—Luck of Roaring Camp—born, 1839

26 Tuesday

Tuskegee Institute President Robert Russa Moton born, 1867
Women got suffrage with Constitutional Amendment XIX, 1920

27 Wednesday

Philosopher Georg W.F. Hegel born, 1770
Novelist Theodore Dreiser—An American Tragedy—born, 1871

28 Thursday

Poet and philosopher Johann Wolfgang von Goethe born, 1749
Painter Sir Edward Burne-Jones born, 1833

29 Friday

Gamesman Edmond Hoyle died, 1769
Poet, philosopher and doctor Oliver Wendell Holmes born, 1809

30 Saturday

Civil rights leader Roy Wilkins born, 1901
Baseball great Ted Williams born, 1918

31 Sunday

Comedian Arthur Godfrey born, 1903

August

Diary

Labor
Day

Monday September 1, 1986

Today's weather:

One Hour of the Day

A Dream Picnic—
Where,
What, With Who?

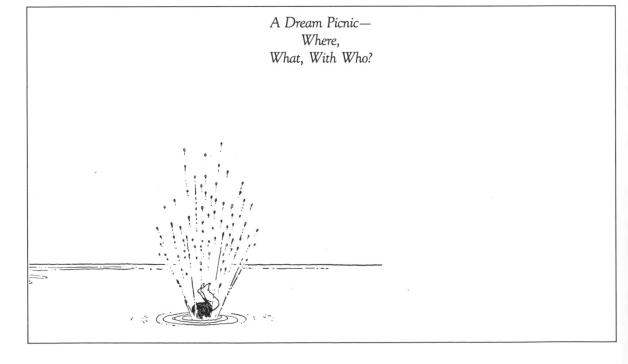

A Memento
of
Labor Day

Why, universal plodding poisons up
　　The nimble spirits in the arteries,
As motion and long-during action tires
　　The sinewy vigour of the traveller.
William Shakespeare, Love's Labour's Lost

EXCELSIOR!

THE DIGNITY OF LABOUR.

Apply This Thought to Skyscrapers

"Grandeur…consists in form, and not in size; and to the eye of the philosopher, the curve drawn on a paper two inches long, is just as magnificent, just as symbolic of divine mysteries and melodies, as when embodied in the span of some cathedral roof."

Charles Kingsley, 1819–1875

Future New York "The city of skyscrapers"

"Plough keep while sluggards sleep."

Benjamin Franklin

September
Sun Mon Tue Wed Thur Fri Sat
1 2 3   4 5 6
7 8 9 10 11 12 13
14 15 16 17 18 19 20
21 22 23 24 25 26 27
28 29 30

Appointments
1 Monday
Labor Day
First Pullman sleeping car in operation, 1860
2 Tuesday
Economist & philosopher Henry George born, 1839
3 Wednesday
Architect Louis Henri Sullivan born, 1856
Merchant and philanthropist Edward Albert Filene born, 1860
4 Thursday
Henry Hudson discovered the island of Manhattan, 1609
Editor and publisher Richard Rogers Bowker born, 1848
5 Friday
Cardinal Richelieu of France born, 1585
First Continental Congress convened in Philadelphia, 1774
6 Saturday
Frenchman and American Revolutionary War hero
Marquis de Lafayette born, 1757
7 Sunday
Beloved naive painter Grandma Moses born, 1860

September

No workman steel, no pond'rous axes rung:
Like some tall palm the noiseless fabric sprung

Bishop Reginald Heber, 1783–1826

Diary

September						
Sun	Mon	Tue	Wed	Thur	Fri	Sat
	1	2	3	4	5	6
7	8	9	10	11	12	13
14	15	16	17	18	19	20
21	22	23	24	25	26	27
28	29	30				

"Only an inventor knows how to borrow, and every man is or should be an inventor."

Ralph Waldo Emerson, from "Quotation and Originality"

"Here, more than anywhere else in the world, the daily panorama of human existence—the unending procession of governmental extortion and chicaneries, of commercial brigandages and throat-slittings, of theological buffooneries, of aesthetic ribaldries, of legal swindles and harlotries—is so inordinately extravagant, so perfectly brought up to the highest conceivable amperage, that only the man who was born with a petrified diaphragm can fail to go to bed every night grinning from ear to ear."

H.L. Mencken, "On Being an American," 1922

Appointments

8 Monday

Actor Peter Sellers born, 1925

9 Tuesday

First giant panda born in captivity, in China, 1963

10 Wednesday

Elias Howe's sewing machine patented, 1846

11 Thursday

Surprise ending short story writer, William Sidney Porter (O. Henry) born, 1862

12 Friday

Rotary printing press inventor Richard March Hoe born, 1812

13 Saturday

Yellow Fever fighter, army surgeon Walter Reed, born, 1851

14 Sunday

Grandparents Day—founded by Marion McQuade & Mike Goldgar, 1978
1780 founder of Sunday School Englishman Robert Raikes born, 1735

September

Diary

September

Sun	Mon	Tue	Wed	Thur	Fri	Sat
	1	2	3	4	5	6
7	8	9	10	11	12	13
14	15	16	17	18	19	20
21	22	23	24	25	26	27
28	29	30				

"Necessity invented stools, convenience next suggested elbow-chairs, and Luxury the accomplish'd Sofa last.

William Cowper

A Branch Library

There is an old fellow named Mark,
Who lives in a tree in the Park.
    You can see him each night,
    By his library light,
Turning over the leaves after dark.

James Montgomery Flagg

On Catching Wasps

"The safest season for experiment is in September. You are now certain to find your wasps in numbers upon the golden-rods....Creep up slyly, hold your open palm within a foot of the insect, and murmur to your inmost self the following brief sentiment,
    '*Polistes! Polistes! bifrons! proponito faciem!*'
and wait until the insect turns towards you, which it is more or less certain to do; then, with a quick clutch, grasp your prize. It is not necessary to hold your breath or wet your fingers....After holding the insect in the hollow of your hand for a moment, take him boldly between your fingers, roll him, pull him, squeeze him, and twirl him as you will; no amount of abuse will induce him to sting....Then let him loose upon the wing, none the worse bodily, even though somewhat richer in experience.

"P.S.—I almost forgot to mention that it is ...safest with *white-faced wasps*, as these are *drones*, and *have no sting*."

William Hamilton Gibson, Sharp Eyes, 1893

Appointments
15 Monday *Novelist James Fenimore Cooper born, 1789* *Pappy Debert born, 1908*
16 Tuesday *The Pilgrims left Plymouth, England, in the "Mayflower," 1620* *Historian and author Hamlin Garland born, 1860*
17 Wednesday *Constitution Day & Citizenship Day. US Constitution signed, 1787* *Mercury vapor lamp invented by Peter Cooper Hewitt, 1901*
18 Thursday *Lexicographer and "literary drudge" Samuel Johnson born, 1709* *Gyroscope inventor Jean Bernard Leon Foucault born, 1819*
19 Friday *Children's book illustrator—Peter Pan—Arthur Rackham born, 1867*
20 Saturday *First electric stove, invented by George B. Simpson, patented, 1859!!*
21 Sunday *H(erbert) G(eorge) Wells, fabulist and novelist, born, 1866*

September

Diary

September

Sun	Mon	Tue	Wed	Thur	Fri	Sat
		1	2	3	4	5 6
7	8	9	10	11	12	13
14	15	16	17	18	19	20
21	22	23	24	25	26	27
28	29	30				

Appointments

22 Monday

Physicist & chemist Michael Faraday born, 1791

23 Tuesday

Autumnal Equinox. Fall begins: 3:59 a.m. EDT
NY's Knickerbockers, America's 1st baseball team, organized, 1845

24 Wednesday

Animal sculptor Antoine Barye born, 1795

25 Thursday

Explorer Balboa discovered the Pacific Ocean, 1513
Yosemite National Park established, 1890

26 Friday

Composer George Gershwin born, 1898

27 Saturday

English cartoonist & illustrator George Cruikshank born, 1792
American cartoonist & illustrator Thomas Nast born, 1840

28 Sunday

Rebecca of Sunnybrook Farm *author Kate Douglas Wiggin born, 1856*

September

Diary

September

Sun Mon Tue Wed Thur Fri Sat
        1 2 3 4 5 6
 7 8 9 10 11 12 13
14 15 16 17 18 19 20
21 22 23 24 25 26 27
28 29 30

Appointments
29 Monday   *Feast of the Archangels: Michael, Gabriel & Raphael*
30 Tuesday   *Feast of St. Jerome—patron saint of scholars & librarians*
1 Wednesday   *Feast of vegetables: World Vegetarian Day 1st celebrated, 1983*
2 Thursday   *Fasting proponent & social reformer Mohandas Gandhi born, 1869*
3 Friday   *Feast-with-manners maven Emily Post born, 1873*
4 Saturday   *Rosh Hashana—Jewish New Year 5747*
5 Sunday   *The Greenpeace Foundation formed in Vancouver, 1970*

"Books are delightful when prosperity happily smiles; when adversity threatens, they are inseparable comforters. They give strength to human compacts, nor are grave opinions brought forward without books. Arts and sciences, the benefits of which no mind can calculate, depend upon books."

Richard Aungervyle, Philobiblon

"It is in the interpretation of natural facts and phenomena that temperament, imagination, emotional sensibility, come in play. In all subjective fields—in religion, politics, art, philosophy—one man's truth may be another man's falsehood, but in the actual concrete world of observation and experience, if we all see correctly, we shall all see alike. Blue is blue and red is red, and our color-blindness does not alter the fact."

John Burroughs, Leaf and Tendril, *1908*

September October

Diary

October

Sun	Mon	Tue	Wed	Thur	Fri	Sat
			1	2	3	4
5	6	7	8	9	10	11
12	13	14	15	16	17	18
19	20	21	22	23	24	25
26	27	28	29	30	31	

Observations in October

In the wane of the Moone, it is good to set yong trees of Apples, Peares, Wardens, Roses, and Berry bushes.

In the wane of the Moone, set Beanes, and Rathe pease, and sowe Parceneps in warme Gardens.

Send out boyes to gather Acorns.

Gather winter fruit.

Bid the boy goe skar the Crowes.

Finish up the Phisick you mind to take and rest till March

Use good hot meates and drinkes.

Go dry-shod lest the Rheum take thee.

Ram's Little Dodoen, 1606

Nine little tailors stitched away, / All cross-legged, and in a row. / "How do you like it?" they were asked; / "Oh," said they, "It is just sew-sew."

Malcolm Douglas, "St. Nicholas" magazine, October 1892

Appointments
6 Monday *Universal Children's Day* *Air brake inventor George Westinghouse born, 1846*
7 Tuesday *Poet & humorist James Whitcomb Riley born, 1849*
8 Wednesday *Aviation hero Edward Vernon Rickenbacker born, 1890*
9 Thursday *Leif Ericsson Day* *Creator of Don Quixote Miguel de Cervantes baptized, 1547*
10 Friday *Historical painter Benjamin West born, 1738* *Actress of historical roles Helen Hayes born, 1900*
11 Saturday *Eleanor Roosevelt born, 1884*
12 Sunday *Christopher Columbus landed in America, 1492*

October

Follow Columbus, or Get Some Get Up and Go!

"Washington Irving tells a story of a man who tried to jump over a hill. He went back so far to get his start for the great leap and ran so hard that he was completely exhausted when he came to the hill, and had to lie down and rest. Then he got up and walked over the hill.

"A great many people exhaust themselves getting ready to do their work. They are always preparing. They spend their lives getting ready to do something which they never do."

O.S. Marden, in Cyclopedia of Illustrations for Public Speakers; *1911*

But oars alone can ne'er prevail
To reach the distant coast;
The breath of Heaven must swell the sail,
Or all the toil is lost.

William Cowper

October						
Sun	Mon	Tue	Wed	Thur	Fri	Sat
			1	2	3	4
5	6	7	8	9	10	11
12	13	14	15	16	17	18
19	20	21	22	23	24	25
26	27	28	29	30	31	

Appointments

13 Monday

Yom Kippur—Day of Atonement
Columbus Day & Discoverers Day
Canadian Thanksgiving (see pages 120–121)

14 Tuesday

Quaker founder of Pennsylvania William Penn born, 1644
Informal birthday of Peace Corps, 1960

15 Wednesday

Gregorian calendar introduced into Roman Catholic countries, 1582
Economist John Kenneth Galbraith born, 1908

16 Thursday

American lexicographer Noah Webster born, 1758
Playwright Eugene O'Neill born, 1888

17 Friday

Albert Einstein immigrated to the US, 1933

18 Saturday

Succoth—Feast of Tabernacles Harvest Festival
English dandy Richard "Beau" Nash born, 1674

19 Sunday

The British surrendered to General Washington at Yorktown, VA, 1781

October

Autumn Days

Yellow, mellow, ripened days,
    Sheltered in a golden coating;
O'er the dreamy, listless haze,
    White and dainty cloudlets floating;
Winking at the blushing trees,
    And the sombre, furrowed fallow;
Smiling at the airy ease.
    Of the southward flying swallow.
Sweet and smiling are thy ways,
Beauteous, golden Autumn days.

Will Carleton

Soul Music

"Music is not a volume of sound; it is an experience which sound transmits from one soul to another soul. The composer creates in himself the symphony. He translates this creation into symbolic language upon a sheet of paper. The orchestra translates this translation."

Lyman Abbott

October

Sun	Mon	Tue	Wed	Thur	Fri	Sat
					1	2	3	4
5	6	7	8	9	10	11
12	13	14	15	16	17	18
19	20	21	22	23	24	25
26	27	28	29	30	31	

Appointments

20 Monday

Philosopher and educator John Dewey born, 1859
Calvin Coolidge coined "A chicken in every pot," 1928

21 Tuesday

Poet Samuel Taylor Coleridge born, 1772
Poet Will Carleton born, 1845

22 Wednesday

Composer and pianist Franz Liszt born, 1811
The Metropolitan Opera House opened with "Faust," 1883

23 Thursday

Swallows leave Capistrano today
Actress Sarah Bernhardt born, 1844

24 Friday

United Nations Day—UN chartered, 1945
Protozoa-perceiver and microscopist van Leeuwenhoek born, 1632

25 Saturday

Explorer and aviator over North Pole, Richard E. Byrd, born, 1888

26 Sunday

Mother-in-Law Day
Daylight Savings ends—Fall back, at 2 a.m.!

October

Diary

Halloween

Friday October 31, 1986

Witching Hour Weather:

A Memento of the Day

Face
for
a
Jack o' Lantern

Things
Not to Be
Frightened Of!

Treats

October

Sun	Mon	Tue	Wed	Thur	Fri	Sat
				1	2	3 4
5	6	7	8	9	10	11
12	13	14	15	16	17	18
19	20	21	22	23	24	25
26	27	28	29	30	31	

LIBERTY
Repaired at Last

"The other day I came down the East River on the steamer. I saw the Bartholdi statue, and my only comment on it, in voice or in thought, was upon its dingy appearance. I wondered that it had not been cleaned. When I sat in my house reading afterward, I came to an account of the ecstasy of an immigrant when first he saw the statue. It was to him the incarnation of all that he had hoped for. Its torch seemed to light his feet to the ways of peace and prosperity. It seemed to be calling a welcome from this land that is free....I wish it might be that we could never see it without similar emotion."

C.B. McAfee, c. 1910

Appointments
27 Monday
US Navy established by Continental Congress, 1775
Violin virtuoso Niccolo Paganini born, 1782
28 Tuesday
Explorer Captain James Cook born, 1728
Statue of Liberty dedicated, 1886
29 Wednesday
British astronomer Edmund Halley born, 1656
Poet John Keats born, 1795
30 Thursday
Sculptor of statuette groups John Rogers born, 1829
31 Friday
Halloween
National Magic Day—Houdini died, 1926
1 Saturday
All Saints Day
Sculptor and goldsmith Benvenuto Cellini born, 1500
2 Sunday
All Souls Day
Explorer Daniel Boone born, 1734

O_{ctober} November

Diary

All-Hallow-Eve.

NOCTURNAL RANGERS,
TAKE

WARNING!

No Signs to be Misplaced
Hereafter.

Growler Watchem.

"Civilization is order and freedom promoting cultural activity."

Will Durant

"You can't say civilization isn't advancing: in every war, they kill you in a new way."

Will Rogers

"The one thing that marks the true artist is a clear perception and a firm, bold hand, in distinction from that imperfect mental vision and uncertain touch which give us the feeble pictures and the lumpy statues of the mere artisans on canvas or in stone."

Oliver Wendell Holmes, The Professor at the Breakfast Table

November

Sun	Mon	Tue	Wed	Thur	Fri	Sat
						1
2	3	4	5	6	7	8
9	10	11	12	13	14	15
16	17	18	19	20	21	22
23	24	25	26	27	28	29
30						

Appointments

3 Monday

Sadie Hawkins Day
Poet and journalist William Cullen Bryant born, 1794

4 Tuesday

Humorist Will Rogers born, 1879

5 Wednesday

Guy Fawkes Day in England
Author and historian Ida M. Tarbell born, 1857

6 Thursday

"The March King" John Philip Sousa born, 1854
Basketball inventor James Naismith born, 1861

7 Friday

Physicist and chemist Madame Marie Curie born, 1867
Al Hirt born, 1923

8 Saturday

Abolitionist Elijah P. Lovejoy born, 1802

9 Sunday

Architect Stanford White born, 1853

November

Diary

| November |
| Sun Mon Tue Wed Thur Fri Sat |
| 1 |
| 2 3 4 5 6 7 8 |
| 9 10 11 12 13 14 15 |
| 16 17 18 19 20 21 22 |
| 23 24 25 26 27 28 29 |
| 30 |

 ## Birds'-Nest Building Materials

White-eyed vireo . . . . Newspaper
Great Crested
Fly-catcher . . . . Snake-skins
Wren . . . . Feathers
Snow-bunting . . . . Fox-hair
Worm-eating warbler . . . . . . Hickory catkins
Ovenbird . . . . Moss spores
Purple finch . . . . Horse-hair
Prairie warbler . . . . Caterpillar-skins
Humming-bird . . . . Fern-wool
Robin . . . . Grass & mud
Baltimore oriole . . . . Milk-weed bark

William Hamilton Gibson, Sharp Eyes, *1893*

Appointments

10 Monday

Religious reformer Martin Luther born, 1483
US Marine Corps founded, 1775

11 Tuesday

Remembrance Day & Veterans Day
Armistice Day—World War I armistice signed, 1918

12 Wednesday

Women's rights leader Elizabeth Cady Stanton born, 1815

13 Thursday

Founder oldest
Paris couturier house Charles Frederick Worth born, 1825

14 Friday

Painter of miniatures & inventor of steamboats,
Robert Fulton, born, 1765

15 Saturday

Pikes Peak discovered by Zebulon Pike, 1806

16 Sunday

Composer Paul Hindemith born, 1895

November

Diary

November

Sun	Mon	Tue	Wed	Thur	Fri	Sat
						1
2	3	4	5	6	7	8
9	10	11	12	13	14	15
16	17	18	19	20	21	22
23	24	25	26	27	28	29
30						

Charm

"'Speaking of Charm,' I said, 'there is one quality which I find very attractive, though most people don't notice it, and rather dislike it if they do. That quality is Observation. You read of it in eighteenth-century books—"a Man of much Observation," they say. So few people,' I went on, 'really notice anything—they live in theories and thin dreams and look dully at you with investigating eyes. They take no real interest in the real world; but the Observers I speak of find it a source of inexhaustible fascination. Nothing escapes them; they can tell at once what the people they meet are like, where they belong, their profession, the kind of houses they live in. The slightest thing is enough for them to judge by—a tone of voice, a gesture, the way they put their hats on.'

"'I always judge people,' one of the company remarked, 'by their shoes. It's people's feet I look at first. And shoe-laces now—what an awful lot shoe-laces can tell you!'

"As I slipped my feet back under my chair, I subjected to a rapid reconsideration my notion of Charm."

Logan Pearsall Smith, All Trivia, 1917

Appointments

17 Monday

Inventor of daguerreotype photography, Louis Daguerre, born, 1789
Suez Canal opened, 1869

18 Tuesday

Botanist Asa Gray born, 1810
Standard time became effective in US, 1883

19 Wednesday

Lincoln made Gettysburg Address, 1863

20 Thursday

Oxfam Fast Day & Great American Smokeout
TV drama host Alistair Cooke born, 1908

21 Friday

Philosopher and historian Voltaire born, 1694
Congressman Dan Glickman introduced Peace Academy bill, 1981

22 Saturday

George Eliot (née Mary Evans)—author Silas Marner—born, 1819

23 Sunday

Harpist and comedian Harpo Marx born, 1893

November

Diary

Thanksgiving Day

(See October 13 and November 27)

Today's weather:

Counted as Blessings

Menu or Special Recipe

A Memento of the Day

Ways to Give Thanks

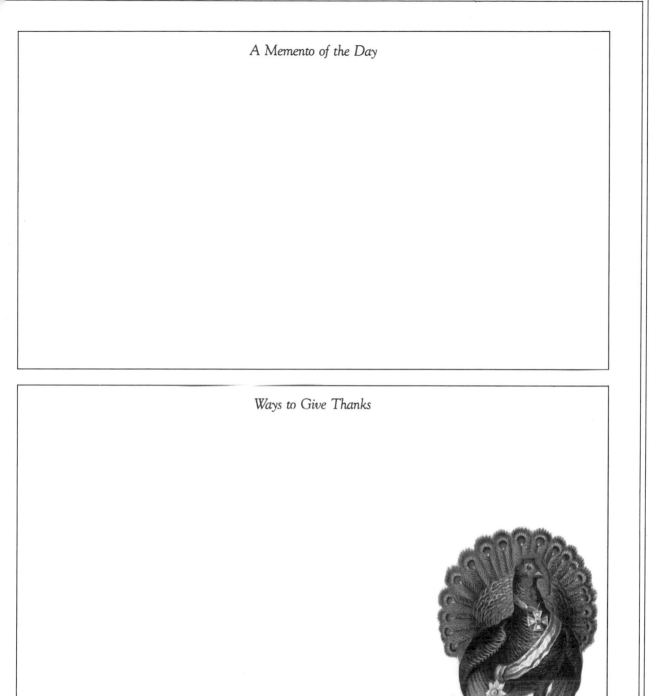

"And we are put on earth a little space that we may learn to bear the beams of love."

William Blake

"What shall I compare it to, this fantastic thing I call my Mind? To a waste-paper basket, to a sieve choked with sediment, or to a barrel full of floating froth and refuse?

"No, what it is really most like is a spider's web, insecurely hung on leaves and twigs, quivering in every wind, and sprinkled with dewdrops and dead flies. And at its geometric centre, pondering for ever the Problem of Existence, sits motionless and spider-like the uncanny Soul."

Logan Pearsall Smith, All Trivia, *1917*

November

Sun	Mon	Tue	Wed	Thur	Fri	Sat
						1
2	3	4	5	6	7	8
9	10	11	12	13	14	15
16	17	18	19	20	21	22
23	24	25	26	27	28	29
30						

Appointments

24 Monday

Philosopher Benedict Spinoza born, 1632

25 Tuesday

Philanthropist & library-funder Andrew Carnegie born, 1838

26 Wednesday

Founder of Harvard College, John Harvard, born, 1607

27 Thursday

Thanksgiving
Actress Fanny Kemble born, 1809

28 Friday

Piano virtuoso Anton Rubinstein born, 1829

29 Saturday

Reformer Wendell Phillips born, 1811
Little Women author Louisa May Alcott born, 1832

30 Sunday

First Sunday of Advent
Satirist of Gulliver's Travels Jonathan Swift born, 1667

November

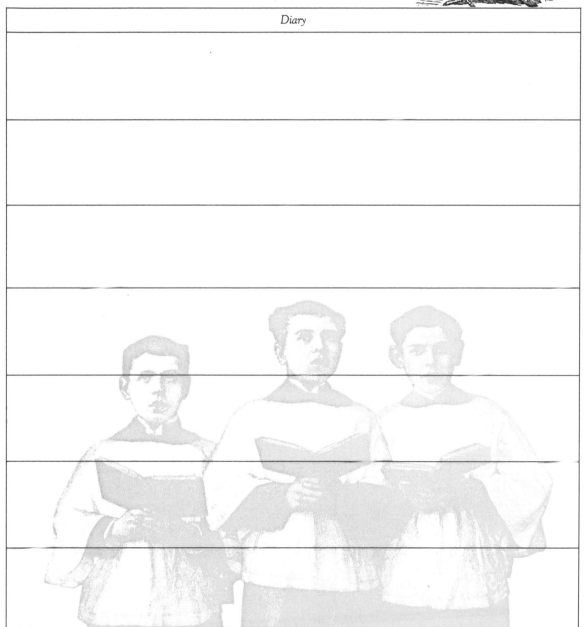

Diary

"In giving freedom to the slave we assure freedom to the free,—honorable alike in what we give and what we preserve."

Abraham Lincoln, 1862

December

Sun	Mon	Tue	Wed	Thur	Fri	Sat
		1	2	3	4	5	6
7	8	9	10	11	12	13
14	15	16	17	18	19	20
21	22	23	24	25	26	27
28	29	30	31			

"What all men are really after is some form, or perhaps only some formula, of peace."

Joseph Conrad

"No thought which I have ever had has satisfied my soul."

Richard Jefferies

Appointments
1 Monday
Author Rex Stout born, 1886
Christmas Seals first sold, 1908
2 Tuesday
Pan American Health Day
Spiritualist baritone Harry Thacker Burleigh born, 1866
3 Wednesday
Portraitist Gilbert Stuart born, 1755
4 Thursday
American Antislavery Society formed, 1833
5 Friday
Poet Christina Rossetti born, 1830
Prohibition repealed, 1933
6 Saturday
Feast of St. Nicholas
Bibliographer Joseph Sabin born, 1821
7 Sunday
Novelist Willa Cather born, 1873

December

Diary

December

Sun Mon Tue Wed Thur Fri Sat

1 2 3 4 5 6
7 8 9 10 11 12 13
14 15 16 17 18 19 20
21 22 23 24 25 26 27
28 29 30 31

A thousand fantasies / Begin to throng into my memory, / Of calling shapes, and beck'ning shadows dire, / And airy tongues that syllable men's names / On sands and shores and desert wildernesses.

John Milton

PIGGY Banks

"Down with the little toy savings-bank! I believe it teaches children to be selfish. I hate to see a child, a sweet, innocent child, with dimpled hands and a laughing face, clutch the penny or the nickel you give it, close in its little fingers, and run first to drop it into the greedy, miserly 'savings-bank,' and then come back to thank you. We teach the child to be selfish when we give it a penny to drop in the missionary-box and fifty cents to buy a toy for itself."

Robert Burdette, c. 1910

Appointments

8 Monday

Inventor Eli Whitney born, 1765
Composer Jean Sibelius born, 1865

9 Tuesday

Poet John Milton born, 1608
Singer & musician Harry Chapin born, 1942

10 Wednesday

Human Rights Day
Nobel Prizes awarded in Sweden today (It's Alfred Nobel's death day)

11 Thursday

Composer Hector Berlioz born, 1803
Discoverer of tuberculosis cause Robert Koch born, 1843

12 Friday

Novelist Gustave Flaubert born, 1821
Poinsettia Day—Death Anniversary of Dr. Joel Poinsett, 1851

13 Saturday

St. Lucia's Day
Poet Heinrich Heine born, 1797

14 Sunday

Astronomer Tycho Brahé born, 1546

December

Diary

December

Sun	Mon	Tue	Wed	Thur	Fri	Sat
		1	2	3	4	5 6
7	8	9	10	11	12	13
14	15	16	17	18	19	20
21	22	23	24	25	26	27
28	29	30	31			

Appointments

15 Monday

The Bill of Rights ratified, 1791

16 Tuesday

Composer Ludwig van Beethoven born, 1770
Novelist Jane Austen born, 1775

17 Wednesday

Chemist Paracelsus born, 1493
Chemist Sir Humphry Davy born, 1778

18 Thursday

Renowned clown Joseph Grimaldi born, 1779
Preacher Lyman Abbott born, 1835

19 Friday

Benjamin Franklin 1st published Poor Richard's Almanac, 1732
Baseball great Ty Cobb born, 1886

20 Saturday

Actress Irene Dunne born, 1904

21 Sunday

Winter Solstice. Winter begins: 11:02 p.m. EST

They's a kind o' *feel* in the air, to me,
When the Chris'mas-times sets in,
That's about as much of a mystery
As ever I've run ag'in!—
Fer instunce, now, whilse I gain in weight
And gineral health, I swear
They's a *goneness* somers I can't quite state—
A kind o' *feel* in the air.

* * *

Is it the racket the children raise?—
W'y, *no!*—God bless 'em—*no!*
Is it the eyes and the cheeks ablaze—
Like my *own* wuz, long ago?—
Is it the bleat o' the whistle and beat
O' the little toy-drum and blare
O' the horn?—*No! No!*—it is jest the sweet—
The sad-sweet feel in the air.

James Whitcomb Riley

December

Diary

Christmas

Thursday December 25, 1986

Today's weather:

Those Who Shared This Day

A Memento of This Holiday

Menu
or
Special
Recipe

A
Christmas
Prayer

Future Discoveries

"In view of the marvelous discoveries which the last half century has witnessed no one can doubt that there is quite as much that is marvelous to come. The dweller on the planet in the year 2000 will undoubtedly look back on these times with a good deal of the same feeling that we of the present day have for those who lived in the days of the stagecoach and the weekly mail; and it is quite likely that the philosopher of that period will speak of ours as 'the good old times.' But however that may be, and whatever the advance they have made in our condition, we may be sure that they will find all their improvements as necessary to existence as we now find the telegraph and railroad and electric. If they have established intercommunication between the planets, they will be just as dependent on those new features as we are on the latest appliances of our civilization."

Detroit Free Press editorial, c. 1910

December

Sun	Mon	Tue	Wed	Thur	Fri	Sat
		1	2	3	4	5 6
7	8	9	10	11	12	13
14	15	16	17	18	19	20
21	22	23	24	25	26	27
28	29	30	31			

Appointments

22 Monday

Founder of Georgia James Edward Oglethorpe born, 1696
Poet Edwin Arlington Robinson born, 1869

23 Tuesday

Opera composer Giacomo Puccini born, 1858
Baseball's "Dean", Connie Mack (Cornelius McGillicuddy), born, 1862

24 Wednesday

Verdi's "Aida" first performed, in Cairo, Egypt, 1871

25 Thursday

Christmas
Nurse Clara Barton born, 1821

26 Friday

Boxing Day
Poet Thomas Gray born, 1716

27 Saturday

Hanukah—Festival of Lights—begins
Bacteriologist Louis Pasteur born, 1822

28 Sunday

Hymn writer Charles Wesley born, 1703

December

Diary

Philanthropy

There are several classes of givers: (1) Those who give spontaneously and generously, but only to themselves; (2) Those who give thoughtlessly, without any real or high motive; (3) Those who give as a sop to conscience and self-esteem, in a species of atonement for the evil they do; (4) Those who give as a matter of display, to win public applause; (5) Those who give because others give, and are ashamed not to give, and therefore give grudgingly: (6) Those who give because they feel they ought to give; who give through a sense of duty, not of love; and (7) Those who give because they love their neighbor as themselves, and above all, desire to help him.

Adapted from a long piece by E.L. Meadows, c. 1910

December

Sun	Mon	Tue	Wed	Thur	Fri	Sat
		1	2	3	4	5 6
7	8	9	10	11	12	13
14	15	16	17	18	19	20
21	22	23	24	25	26	27
28	29	30	31			

Appointments

29 Monday

English Prime Minister William Gladstone born, 1809
Cellist Pablo Casals born, 1876

30 Tuesday

Philanthropist Simon Guggenheim born, 1867
Humorist Stephen Leacock born, 1869

31 Wednesday

New Year's Eve. Be careful!

1 Thursday

New Year's Day. Happy 1987!

2 Friday

Patriot Paul Revere born, 1735

3 Saturday

March of Dimes organized, 1938

4 Sunday

Mathematician Sir Isaac Newton born, 1642

December January

Birthdays

Birthdays come but once a year,
  Leap birthdays once in four.
May all the birthdays listed here
  Be followed by many more!
May all the blessings of the day
  Continue through the year.
Let's not forget to yearly say
  "Oh! Happy Birthday, dear!"

Weddings & Anniversaries

Love makes the world go 'round;
That's what the poets and songsters say.
After many turns, here will be found
The record of '86's loving days!

Graduations, Promotions & Milestone Days

The marching, gleaming milestones,
  Are seen through passing years,
Well-lit by lamps of memory,
  Made bright by lens of tears.
An accident of fortune,
  Some beam that crooks in time,
They'll light a day—quite like the rest—
  But give it extra shine.
Throughout the years these special days
  Will gleam in midnight skies.
And late, and long, remember them;
  They're the milestones in our lives.
Grace McFarland

The Language of Flowers

Sentiments can be expressed through the exchange of flowers. in a 19th century book on etiquette, the following unconcluded "conversation" was given.

The gentleman presents a red rose—"I love you." The lady admits a partial reciprocation of the sentiment by returning a purple pansy—"You occupy my thoughts." The gentleman presses his suit still further by an everlasting pea—"Wilt thou go with me?" The lady replies by a daisy, in which she says—"I will think of it."

Below are but a few of the scores of flowers, herbs and evergreens given meaning.

Acacia *Friendship*

Amaryllis *Beautiful but timid*

Anemone *Forsaken*

Apple Blossom *Preference*

Arbutus *Thee only do I love*

Aster *Variety*

Bachelors' Button *Hope*

Buttercup *Riches*

Camellia *Gratitude*

Carnation *Pure and deep love*

Chrysanthemum *A desolate heart*

Four-Leaved Clover *Be mine*

Red Clover *Industry*

Columbine *Anxious and trembling*

Cowslip *Native grace*

Dahlia *Dignity and elegance*

Daffodil *Unrequited love*

Daisy *I will think about it*

Dandelion *Coquetry*

Forget-me-not *Do not forget*

Fuchsia *Taste or frugality*

Geranium *I prefer you*

Gladiolus *Ready armed*

Hawthorn *Hope*

Hibiscus *Delicate beauty*

Holly *Am I forgotten?*

Hyacinth *Constancy*

Hydrangea *Heartlessness*

Iris *A message for thee*

Jonquil *Desire*

Larkspur *Lightness or fickleness*

Purple Lilac *First emotions of love*

White Lilac *Youth*

Lily of the Valley *Return of happiness*

Magnolia *Love of nature*

Marigold *Sacred affection*

Morning Glory *Affection*

Nasturtium *Patriotism*

Pennyroyal *Flee away*

Phlox *Our hearts are united*

Poppy *Consolation*

Primrose *Modest worth or silent love*

Rhododendron *Agitation*

Red Rose *I love you*

White Rose *Silence*

Wild Rose *Simplicity*

Yellow Rose *Unfaithfulness*

Rue *Disdain*

Snapdragon *Presumption*

Sunflower *Lofty and wise thoughts*

Sweet Pea *A meeting*

Sweet William *Gallantry*

Thorn Apple *Disguise*

Violet *Faithfulness*

Wall Flower *Fidelity in misfortune*

Water Lily *Eloquence*

Zinnia *I mourn your absence*

Birthstones & Flowers

January
 Garnet
 Carnation or Snowdrop
February
 Amethyst
 Primrose or Violet
March
 Aquamarine or Bloodstone
 Jonquil or Daffodil
April
 Diamond
 Daisy or Sweet Pea
May
 Emerald
 Hawthorn or Lily of the Valley
June
 Moonstone, Alexandrite or Pearl
 Rose or Honeysuckle
July
 Ruby
 Water Lily, Larkspur or Delphinium
August
 Peridot or Sardonyx
 Gladiolus or Poppy
September
 Sapphire
 Morning Glory or Aster
October
 Opal or Tourmaline
 Calendula or Marigold
November
 Topaz
 Chrysanthemum
December
 Turquoise or Zircon
 Holly, Narcissus or Poinsettia

Gifts for Wedding Anniversaries

It has long been the custom to give anniversary gifts. As it is expected that gold be given to the celebrating couple on their 50th—Golden—Anniversary, so it has evolved that all the anniversaries up to the fifteenth have special gifts, and every fifth one beyond that also has an appropriate gift. Those couples who celebrate beyond their 75th Anniversary surely have the most precious gift of all—their lasting love for each other.

1st	Paper or plastic	14th	Ivory or agate
2nd	Cotton	15th	Crystal
3rd	Leather	20th	Porcelain or china
4th	Silk or linen	25th	Silver
5th	Wood	30th	Pearl
6th	Iron	35th	Coral or jade
7th	Wool, copper or brass	40th	Ruby or garnet
8th	Electric appliances	45th	Sapphire or
9th	Pottery		tourmaline
10th	Tin or aluminum	50th	Gold
11th	Steel	55th	Emerald or turquoise
12th	Linen or silk	60th	Diamond
13th	Lace	75th	Diamond

Musings
on the Year

"Gone—glimmering through the dream of things that were" (Lord Byron)...to *"The never-ending flight of future days"* (John Milton).

1986

January
Sun	Mon	Tue	Wed	Thu	Fri	Sat
			1	2	3	4
5	6	7	8	9	10	11
12	13	14	15	16	17	18
19	20	21	22	23	24	25
26	27	28	29	30	31	

February
Sun	Mon	Tue	Wed	Thu	Fri	Sat
						1
2	3	4	5	6	7	8
9	10	11	12	13	14	15
16	17	18	19	20	21	22
23	24	25	26	27	28	

March
Sun	Mon	Tue	Wed	Thu	Fri	Sat
						1
2	3	4	5	6	7	8
9	10	11	12	13	14	15
16	17	18	19	20	21	22
23/30	24/31	25	26	27	28	29

April
Sun	Mon	Tue	Wed	Thu	Fri	Sat
		1	2	3	4	5
6	7	8	9	10	11	12
13	14	15	16	17	18	19
20	21	22	23	24	25	26
27	28	29	30			

May
Sun	Mon	Tue	Wed	Thu	Fri	Sat
				1	2	3
4	5	6	7	8	9	10
11	12	13	14	15	16	17
18	19	20	21	22	23	24
25	26	27	28	29	30	31

June
Sun	Mon	Tue	Wed	Thu	Fri	Sat
1	2	3	4	5	6	7
8	9	10	11	12	13	14
15	16	17	18	19	20	21
22	23	24	25	26	27	28
29	30					

July
Sun	Mon	Tue	Wed	Thu	Fri	Sat
		1	2	3	4	5
6	7	8	9	10	11	12
13	14	15	16	17	18	19
20	21	22	23	24	25	26
27	28	29	30	31		

August
Sun	Mon	Tue	Wed	Thu	Fri	Sat
					1	2
3	4	5	6	7	8	9
10	11	12	13	14	15	16
17	18	19	20	21	22	23
24/31	25	26	27	28	29	30

September
Sun	Mon	Tue	Wed	Thu	Fri	Sat
	1	2	3	4	5	6
7	8	9	10	11	12	13
14	15	16	17	18	19	20
21	22	23	24	25	26	27
28	29	30				

October
Sun	Mon	Tue	Wed	Thu	Fri	Sat
			1	2	3	4
5	6	7	8	9	10	11
12	13	14	15	16	17	18
19	20	21	22	23	24	25
26	27	28	29	30	31	

November
Sun	Mon	Tue	Wed	Thu	Fri	Sat
						1
2	3	4	5	6	7	8
9	10	11	12	13	14	15
16	17	18	19	20	21	22
23/30	24	25	26	27	28	29

December
Sun	Mon	Tue	Wed	Thu	Fri	Sat
	1	2	3	4	5	6
7	8	9	10	11	12	13
14	15	16	17	18	19	20
21	22	23	24	25	26	27
28	29	30	31			

1987

January
Sun	Mon	Tue	Wed	Thu	Fri	Sat
				1	2	3
4	5	6	7	8	9	10
11	12	13	14	15	16	17
18	19	20	21	22	23	24
25	26	27	28	29	30	31

February
Sun	Mon	Tue	Wed	Thu	Fri	Sat
1	2	3	4	5	6	7
8	9	10	11	12	13	14
15	16	17	18	19	20	21
22	23	24	25	26	27	28

March
Sun	Mon	Tue	Wed	Thu	Fri	Sat
1	2	3	4	5	6	7
8	9	10	11	12	13	14
15	16	17	18	19	20	21
22	23	24	25	26	27	28
29	30	31				

April
Sun	Mon	Tue	Wed	Thu	Fri	Sat
			1	2	3	4
5	6	7	8	9	10	11
12	13	14	15	16	17	18
19	20	21	22	23	24	25
26	27	28	29	30		

May
Sun	Mon	Tue	Wed	Thu	Fri	Sat
					1	2
3	4	5	6	7	8	9
10	11	12	13	14	15	16
17	18	19	20	21	22	23
24/31	25	26	27	28	29	30

June
Sun	Mon	Tue	Wed	Thu	Fri	Sat
	1	2	3	4	5	6
7	8	9	10	11	12	13
14	15	16	17	18	19	20
21	22	23	24	25	26	27
28	29	30				

July
Sun	Mon	Tue	Wed	Thu	Fri	Sat
			1	2	3	4
5	6	7	8	9	10	11
12	13	14	15	16	17	18
19	20	21	22	23	24	25
26	27	28	29	30	31	

August
Sun	Mon	Tue	Wed	Thu	Fri	Sat
						1
2	3	4	5	6	7	8
9	10	11	12	13	14	15
16	17	18	19	20	21	22
23/30	24/31	25	26	27	28	29

September
Sun	Mon	Tue	Wed	Thu	Fri	Sat
		1	2	3	4	5
6	7	8	9	10	11	12
13	14	15	16	17	18	19
20	21	22	23	24	25	26
27	28	29	30			

October
Sun	Mon	Tue	Wed	Thu	Fri	Sat
				1	2	3
4	5	6	7	8	9	10
11	12	13	14	15	16	17
18	19	20	21	22	23	24
25	26	27	28	29	30	31

November
Sun	Mon	Tue	Wed	Thu	Fri	Sat
1	2	3	4	5	6	7
8	9	10	11	12	13	14
15	16	17	18	19	20	21
22	23	24	25	26	27	28
29	30					

December
Sun	Mon	Tue	Wed	Thu	Fri	Sat
		1	2	3	4	5
6	7	8	9	10	11	12
13	14	15	16	17	18	19
20	21	22	23	24	25	26
27	28	29	30	31		

Index

This is a do-it-yourself index for your 1986 Diary. Use it to note the really important days you want to be able to look up quickly, or the sweet whimsies of everyday life—the first bluebird's day under "B," the last rose under "R."

A•B	C•D	E•F
G•H	I•J	K•L
M•N	O•P	Q•R
S•T	U•V•W	X•Y•Z